The Gingerbread Man

Autumn
Publishing

Once upon a time, there was a **little** old **lady** who **loved** gingerbread.

One day, she made a **little** gingerbread man. She **lit** the oven to bake it.

Focus on the **l** sound (as in **lady**) as you read.

Lovely!

2

l

Can you spot these 5 items somewhere in the scene?

Place the stickers from your sticker sheet here as you find each one.

ladder

lamp

lemon

lid

stool

Well done

l

l

3

The old lady **b**ent down to put the ginger**b**read man in the oven. **B**ut **b**efore she could close the door, he **b**ounced onto the floor.

Focus on the **b** sound (as in **b**read) as you read.

Then, the ginger**b**read man ran out of the **b**right **b**lue door.

b

Can you spot these 5 items somewhere in the scene?

Place the stickers from your sticker sheet here as you find each one.

basket

book

boots

bread

buttons

Good job

b

5

The gingerbread man ran away from the old lady.

He ran right out of the kitchen. He ran past a rabbit and a red robin in the garden.

Focus on the r sound (as in run) as you read.

Run, run, as fast as you can. You can't catch me, I'm the gingerb**r**ead man!

7

r

Can you spot these 5 items somewhere in the scene?

Place the stickers from your sticker sheet here as you find each one.

rabbit

ring

roses

ray

t**r**icycle

Nice work

r

As he ran **d**own the roa**d**, the gingerbrea**d** man met a **d**og.

"Stop, little gingerbrea**d** man, stop!" sai**d** the **d**og. "You can be my **d**inner."

Focus on the **d** sound (as in **d**og) as you read.

8

I **d**on't think so! **D**ogs **d**on't eat gingerbrea**d**.

Can you spot these 5 items somewhere in the scene?

Place the stickers from your sticker sheet here as you find each one.

bir**d**

dog

doll

duck

woo**d**

Well done

d

9

"Catch me, catch me,
catch me if you can.
You can't catch me, I'm the
gingerbread man!" he sang,
as he carried on his way.

Focus on
the c sound
(as in cat)
as you read.

Cats can't
catch clever
gingerbread men!

10

c

Can you spot these 5 items somewhere in the scene?

Place the stickers from your sticker sheet here as you find each one.

acorn

cake

candle

carrots

s**c**ooter

Good job

c

c

11

The gingerbread man saw a **g**oat by a **g**ate.
"Stop, little gingerbread man," said the **g**oat.
"You look **g**ood to eat!"

Focus on
the **g** sound
(as in **g**oat)
as you read.

It's just **g**rass
for tea a**g**ain!

"I've **g**ot to **g**o!" said the little gingerbread man.
The **g**oat felt **g**rumpy.

g

Can you spot these 5 items somewhere in the scene?

Place the stickers from your sticker sheet here as you find each one.

gate

goose

grapes

pi**g**

goat

Nice work

g

13

Before long, the gingerbread man ran past a forest of fir trees and a fish pond full of frogs.

"Faster, faster, faster, I'm free! You can follow me forever but you won't catch me!" sang the little gingerbread man.

Focus on the f sound (as in frog) as you read.

Look at that funny little gingerbread man flying by!

Can you spot these 5 items somewhere in the scene?

Place the stickers from your sticker sheet here as you find each one.

dragonfly

fish

fly

frog

leaf

Well done

f

15

The gingerbread man passed a **h**orse with some **h**ay.
"Stop, little gingerbread man. I am **h**ungry!" said the **h**orse.
"**H**a-ha! **H**ave a nice day!" said the gingerbread man.

Focus on the **h** sound (as in **h**orse) as you read.

Humph! **H**ay for dinner again. **H**ow I'd like to **h**ave something tasty, maybe **h**oney!

Reward stars

Sticker Sounds

Well

done

Good

job

Nice

work

Page 27

Well

done

Good

job

Well

done

h

Can you spot these 5 items somewhere in the scene?

Place the stickers from your sticker sheet here as you find each one.

hat

hay

hen

hive

horse

Good

job

h

17

Soon, the gingerbread man **s**aw a **s**tream, but he couldn't **s**wim.

He **s**aw a fox with a nice **s**mile who was about to cro**ss**.

Focus on the **s** sound (as in **s**nake) as you read.

Sit on me. I can **s**wim.

18

s

Can you spot these 5 items somewhere in the scene?

Place the stickers from your sticker sheet here as you find each one.

snake

snail

squirrel

stick

stone

Nice

work

s

19

Focus on the **o** sound (as in r**o**ck) as you read.

20

The fox began to cross the stream. Then, the stream got deeper. It nearly sploshed the gingerbread man off the fox.

Hop on to the top of my head.

Can you spot these 5 items somewhere in the scene?

Place the stickers from your sticker sheet here as you find each one.

fox

log

otter

rock

rod

Well done

21

Soon, the water was nearly up to the gingerbread man's neck. "Are we nearly there yet?" asked the gingerbread man.

"Nearly," said the fox. "Why not hop on to my nose?"

Focus on the n sound (as in nest) as you read.

22

I'm **n**ot so sure about this **n**ow!

n

Can you spot these 5 items somewhere in the scene?

Place the stickers from your sticker sheet here as you find each one.

ant

bra**n**ch

nest

newt

nose

Good job

n

23

The fox flicked back his neck and opened his mouth. With a quick SNAP! the gingerbread man became a tasty snack.

Focus on the ck sound (as in chick) as you read.

That was lucky. Now I need a toothpick.

24

The smart fox li**ck**ed his lips. That was the end of the gingerbread man.

ck

Can you spot these 5 items somewhere in the scene?

Place the stickers from your sticker sheet here as you find each one.

bri**ck**s

chi**ck**

li**ck**

sa**ck**

so**ck**s

Nice work

ck

25

First Letter Lines

Follow the lines to join the pictures to the correct words, then say the sound each one starts with.

horse

dog

cat

Rhyming Pictures

Match up each picture on the left to one that rhymes with it on the right.

sun

hat

stick

dog

log

chick

bun

cat

Sticker Sounds

Find a sticker from your sticker sheet that starts with the same sound as each of these pictures.

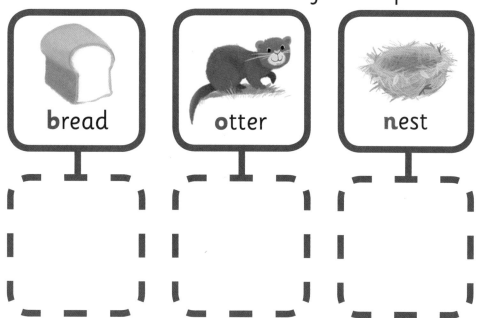

bread   **o**tter   **n**est

Letter Jumble

Count how many times you can see the letter **r**, as in **r**abbit, **r**ing and **r**oses.

Picture Match

Can you join up each picture with the letter it starts with?

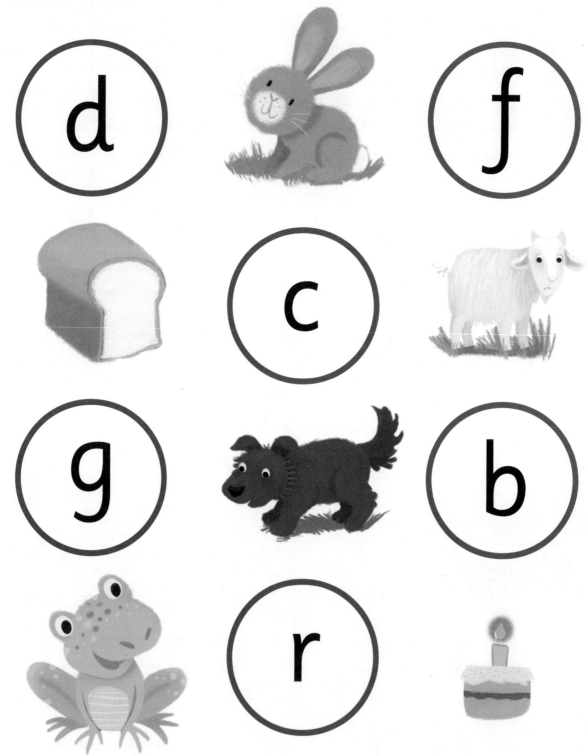

Say the Sounds

Look at the picture and say all the things that start with the **h** sound, as in **h**orse.

Tell a Story

Look at the pictures and tell the story from memory.
What sounds can you remember?

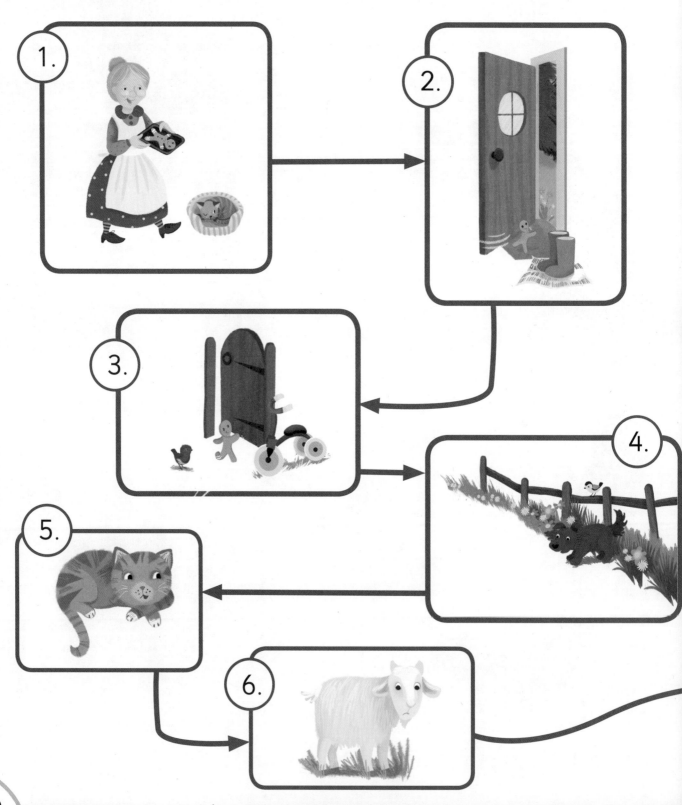

Phonic Moments

Fill in the key sound words for each picture below.
What happened in these parts of the story?